■ EASY START ■

The fun run

Written by Keith Gaines

Illustrated by Nina O'Connell

Nelson

"Get set.

Go,"

said Sam the fox.

Bang,

went the gun.

2

Meg the hen,

Ben the dog,

Jip the cat

and Pat the pig

set off on the Fun Run.

"The sun is hot and
I am hot.
I don't want to run,"
said Pat the pig.
"I want to sit in the sun."

4

"It is fun to run,"

said Meg, Ben and Jip.

"Run, Pat, run,"
said Sam the fox.
"Don't sit in the sun."

"I am a fat pig,"

said Pat the pig.

"It is not fun to run.

It is fun to sit in the sun."

"Pat the pig will not run,"
said Sam.

"I can get him to run,"
said Deb.

"We can run,"

said Meg, Ben and Jip.

"I can run,"
said Pat the pig.
"It is fun."

"Pat can run,"
said Sam.
"He can run
to get a ...

... bun."